Alpha Worship
Songbook

Published 1997

Published by HTB Publications
Holy Trinity Brompton, Brompton Road, London SW7 1JA

Contents

Praise To The Lord

J. Neander 1680
Piano Arr. Alison Berry

Flowing
MM ♩ = 108

Come ye who hear, bro-thers and sis-ters draw near,
Hast thou not seen all that is need-ful hath been
Pon-der a-new all the Al-might-y can do,
Let the "A-men!" sound from His peo-ple a-gain,

praise Him in glad a-do-ra-tion.
grant-ed in what He or-dain-eth?
He who, with love, doth be-friend thee.
glad-ly, for aye, we ad-ore Him.

Give Thanks With A Grateful Heart

Henry Smith
Piano Arr. Alison Berry

3

When I Survey

Words: Issac Watts
Tune: Rockingham
Piano Arr. Alison Berry

5

Here Is Love

Words: W. Rees, W. Edwards; Music : R. Lowry
Piano Arr. Alison Berry

Flowing
MM ♩ = 78

To End go to ⊕

Here is
On the

love vast as the o - cean, lov -ing kind - ness as the flood, when the
mount of cru - ci - fix-ion foun-tains op - ened deep and wide; through the

Prince of Life, our ran -som, shed for us His precious blood. Who His
flood - gates of God's mer-cy flowed a vast and gra-cious tide. Grace and

love will not re- mem-ber, who can cease to sing His praise? He can
love, like might-y riv-ers, poured in- cess - ant from a - bove; and heaven's

ne- ver be for-got-ten throughout heav'n's e-ter-nal days.
peace and per-fect jus-tice kissed a guil - ty world in love.

Praise God From
Whom All Blessings Flow

Andy Piercy & Dave Clifton
Piano Arr. Alison Berry

9

10

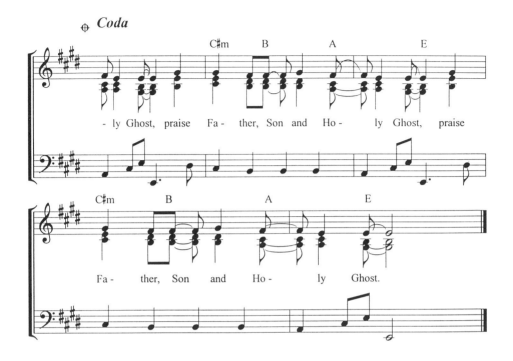

- ly Ghost, praise Fa - ther, Son and Ho - ly Ghost, praise

Fa - ther, Son and Ho - ly Ghost.

11

Give Your Thanks To The Risen Son

Fairly Fast
MM ♩ = 112

Dave Bilbrough
Piano Arr. Alison Berry

E

Turn to Him, don't be a - fraid,   (Turn to Him, don't be a - fraid),

F#m7

Give Him ho - nour, give Him   praise,   (Give Him ho - nour give Him praise),

B

Lift Him up   to the high - est   place,   (Lift Him up   to the high - est   place),

E

Je -   sus,   (Je -   sus),

13

Wor - ship Him, Crown Him King, and give Him all your heart.

1.

2. heart. *Da Capo* heart. **To end**

Amazing Grace

John Newton
Piano Arr. Alison Berry

MM ♩ = 96

F B♭

1. A - maz - ing grace, how sweet the
2. 'Twas grace that taught my heart to
3. Through ma - ny dan - gers, toils and

F G⁷ Csus⁴

sound that saved a wretch like me;
fear and grace my fears re - lieved;
snares I have al - rea - dy come;

C F F/A

I once was lost but
How pre - cious did that
'tis grace that brought me

B♭ F F/E Dm

now am found, was blind but
grace ap - -pear the hour I
safe thus far and grace will

15

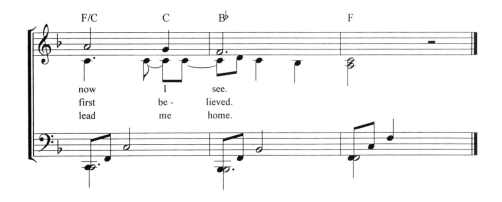

now   I   see.
first   be - lieved.
lead   me   home.

4. The Lord has promised good to me,
   His Word my hope secures;
   He will my shield and portion be
   As long as life endures.

5. Yet when this heart and flesh will fail
   And mortal life shall cease,
   I shall possess within the veil
   A life of joy and peace.

6. When we've been there ten thousand years
   Bright shining as the sun,
   We've no less days to sing God's praise
   Than when we've first begun.

Almighty God

17

God is Our Refuge and Our Strength

Dave Clifton
Piano Arr. Alison Berry

19

We Worship And Adore You

Andy Piercy
Words for V.3: C. F.Alexander
Piano Arr. Alison Berry

Lively
MM ♩ = 140

Capo 3rd Fret

We wor-ship and a-dore You, Lord, hear us when we call, for there is no god a-bove -You, You are the Lord of all. 1. But

how can we be-gin to ex-press what's on our hearts?
-of men and an-gels we need, to sing Your praise,

There are not words e-nough, Lord, for
so that we may glo-ri-fy Your Name through

21

us to e - ven start.   2. The tongues   3. There
heav'ns e - ter - nal days.

was no o - ther good e - nough to pay the price of sin,

You on - ly, could un - lock the gate of

D.S. al Coda

heaven and let us in. So we wor - ship and a - dore

Coda F

The Lord Reigns

Lively but steady
MM ♩ = 96

Dan Stradwick
Piano Arr. Alison Berry

The Lord reigns, (The Lord reigns), Let the earth rejoice, (Let the earth rejoice). The Lord Right-eous - ness and truth, (Right- eous- ness and truth), Are the foun- da- tions of Your throne, (Are the foun- da- tions of Your throne; Right- eous- ness and truth, (Right- eous- ness and

23

truth) Are the foun- da- tions of Your throne.

In Your pre- sence Lord, (In Your pre-sence Lord), The mountains melt like

1. wax, (The mountains melt like wax). In Your pre- sence **2.** wax. In Your pre-sence

Lord, (In Your pre-sence Lord), I bow before Your throne, (I bow before Your

throne), In Your pres- ence Lord, (In Your pres- ence Lord) (all) I bow before Your

I Lift My Eyes Up

Brian Doerksen
Piano Arr. Alison Berry

Flowing
MM ♩ = 66

Last time go to 𝄋.

I lift my eyes up to the moun - tains: where does my help come from? My help comes from You, Ma-ker of hea - ven, Cre -a -tor of the earth. Oh, how I need You Lord, You are my on - ly hope, You're my on - ly

prayer; so, I will wait for You to come and res - cue me, come and give me life. earth.

Father God

Steady
MM ♩ = 70

Ian Smale
Piano Arr. Alison Berry

Fa-ther God I won-der how I managed to ex-ist without the knowledge of Your parenthood and Your loving care. But now I am Your child I am a-dop-ted in Your fam-i-ly and I can ne-ver be a-lone, 'cause Fa-ther God You're there beside me. I will sing Your prai-ses, I will sing Your prai-ses, I will sing Your prai-ses for-e-ver-more. for-ever-more.

Every Day

Leslie Phillips
Piano Arr. Alison Berry

29

Sing To The Lord

I Have Found Such Joy In My Salvation

Marc Nelson
Piano Arr. Alison Berry

I wor-ship You, wor- ship You my Lord.

Last time

33

PRAISE TO THE LORD

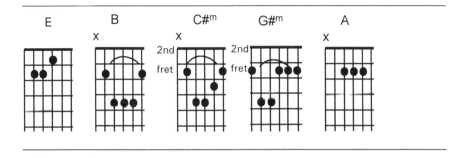

E   B   C#^m   G#^m   A

```
 E      B   C#m     G#m A
Praise to the Lord the Almighty
  E    A       B E
The King of creation
E      B    C#m
O my soul, praise Him
  G#m A  E   A            B E
For He is thy health and salvation
                 A
Come ye who hear
  C#m          A         B
Brothers and sisters draw near
  E           C#m    B E
Praise Him in glad adoration
```

Praise to the Lord, who o'er all
Things so wondrously reigneth
Shelters thee under His wings,
Yea, so gently sustaineth:
Hast thou not seen
All that is needful hath been
Granted in what He ordaineth?

Praise to the Lord, who doth
Prosper thy work and defend thee
Surely His goodness and
Mercy shall daily attend thee:
Ponder anew
All the Almighty can do,
He who with love doth befriend thee

Praise to the Lord, O let all
That is in me adore Him
All that hath life and breath
Come now with praises before Him
Let the amen
Sound from His people again
Gladly for aye we adore him

J Neander 1680 Public Domain

GIVE THANKS WITH A GRATEFUL HEART

　　　　E　　　　　　　　B
Give thanks with a grateful heart
　　　　C#ᵐ　　　　　　G#ᵐ
Give thanks to the Holy One
　　　　A　　　　　　　　　　　E　　　　D　　　B
Give thanks because He's given Jesus Christ, His Son　(x2)

　　　G#ᵐ　　　　　C#ᵐ　　　　　　F#ᵐ
And now, let the weak say "I am strong"
　　　B　　　　　　　Eᵐᵃʲ⁷
Let the poor say "I am rich"
　　　　　C#ᵐ　　　　　　　　D　　　B
Because of what the Lord has done for us

　　　　　　　　　　　　　　　　　　　　　(x2)

E　　　　　　　Eˢᵘˢ⁴　　　　E
Give thanks　　Give thanks

Henry Smith © 1978 Integrity's Hosanna! Music / Kingsway's Thankyou Music

WHEN I SURVEY THE WONDROUS CROSS

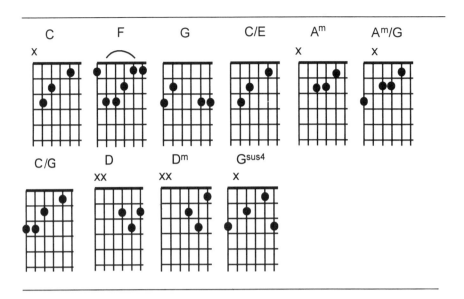

```
     C  CF G   C        C/E   F    C
When I survey the wondrous cross
G/B  A^m  A^m/G  F     C/E  D^mC  G^sus4  G
On which   the   Prince of   glory died
     G    D   G     C    D   G
My richest gain I count but loss
C    F    C/E   D^m   C  C/G G  C
And pour contempt on all  my pride


Forbid it, Lord, that I should boast
Save in the death of Christ my God
All the vain things that charm me most
I sacrifice them to His blood
```

See from His head, His hands, His feet
Sorrow and love flow mingled down
Did e'er such love and sorrow meet
Or thorns compose so rich a crown

Were the whole realm of nature mine
That were an offering far too small
Love so amazing, so divine
Demands my life, my soul, my all

I Watts 1707
Public Domain

HERE IS LOVE

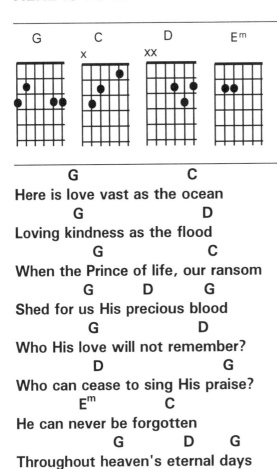

G   C   D   Eᵐ

         G   C
Here is love vast as the ocean
        G   D
Loving kindness as the flood
           G   C
When the Prince of life, our ransom
          G   D   G
Shed for us His precious blood
          G   D
Who His love will not remember?
          D   G
Who can cease to sing His praise?
         Eᵐ   C
He can never be forgotten
               G   D   G
Throughout heaven's eternal days

On the mount of crucifixion
Fountains opened deep and wide
Through the floodgates of God's mercy
Flowed a vast and gracious tide
Grace and love, like mighty rivers
Poured incessant from above
And heaven's peace and perfect justice
Kissed a guilty world in love

William Rees Public Domain

PRAISE GOD FROM WHOM ALL BLESSINGS FLOW

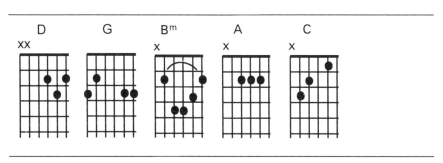

E
Capo 2nd fret (D)

    E(D)   A(G)   E(D)
Praise God from whom all blessings flow
    C#^{m}(B^m) B(A)   A(G)   E(D)
Praise Him all   creatures here below
    E(D)   A(G)   E(D)
Praise Him above you heavenly host
    C#^{m}(B^m) B(A)   A(G) E(D)
Praise Father,   Son and Holy Ghost

    B(A)   E(D)
Give glory to the Father, give glory to the Son
    A(G)   C#^{m}(B^m)   A(G)   B(A)
Give glory to the Spirit while endless ages run

    B(A)   E(D)
"Worthy the Lamb" all heaven cries, to be exalted thus
   A(G)   C#^{m}(B^m)
"Worthy the Lamb" our hearts reply
   A(G)   D(C)   B(A)
For He was slain for us

A Piercy & D Clifton © 1993 IQ Music

GIVE YOUR THANKS TO THE RISEN SON

E
Give Your thanks to the risen Son   (echo)
    F#ᵐ
To the Holy and Anointed One   (echo)
    B
Who fills our hearts with a joyful song,   (echo)
E
Jesus   (echo)

E
Turn to Him, don't be afraid   (echo)
F#ᵐ
Give Him honour, give Him praise   (echo)
B
Lift him up to the highest place   (echo)
  E
Jesus

E   F#ᵐ
Worship Him Crown Him King
    B   E
And give Him all your heart   (x2)

Dave Bilbrough © 1994 Kingsway's Thankyou Music

AMAZING GRACE

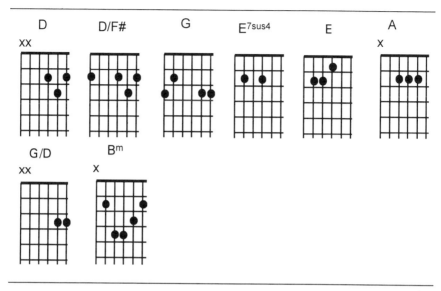

F
Capo third fret (D)

  F(D)   F/A(D/F#)   B♭(G)   F(D)
Amazing Grace   how sweet the sound
         G (E^{7sus4}) G(E) C(A)
That saved a wretch like me
 F(D)   F/A(D/F#)   B♭(G)   F(D)
I once was lost   but   now am found
     D^m (B^m)   F(D) C(A) B♭/F(G/D) F(D)
Was blind but now I   see

'Twas grace that taught my heart to fear
And grace my fears relieved
How precious did that grace appear
The hour I first believed

Through many dangers, toils and snares
I have already come
'Tis grace that brought me safe thus far
And grace will lead me home

When we've been there ten thousand years
Bright shining as the sun
We've no less days to sing God's praise
Than when we've first begun

John Newton (1725-1807)
Public Domain

ALMIGHTY GOD

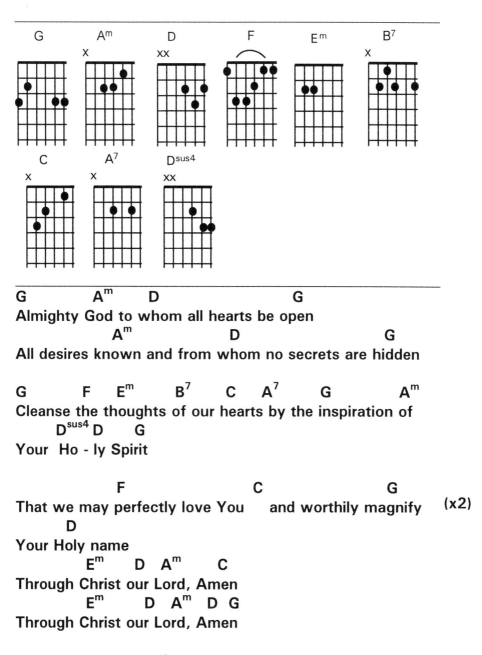

G   A^m   D   G

G   A^m   D   G

Almighty God to whom all hearts be open

A^m D   G

All desires known and from whom no secrets are hidden

G   F E^m   B⁷   C A⁷   G   A^m

Cleanse the thoughts of our hearts by the inspiration of

D^{sus4} D   G

Your Ho - ly Spirit

F   C   G

That we may perfectly love You   and worthily magnify   **(x2)**

D

Your Holy name

E^m   D A^m   C

Through Christ our Lord, Amen

E^m   D A^m D G

Through Christ our Lord, Amen

A Piercy, D Clifton & C Groves © 1994 I.Q. Music
Words - Alternative Service Book 1980
The Central Board of Finance of the Church of England

GOD IS OUR REFUGE

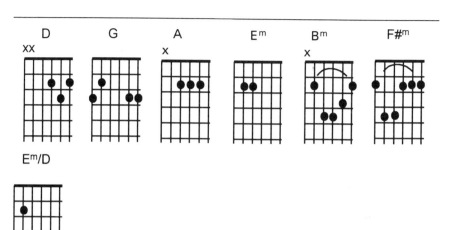

E(D)   A(G)   B(A)
God is our refuge and our strength

E
Capo 2nd fret (D)

   F#ᵐ(Eᵐ)   B(A)   E(D)   A(G) B(A) (link to
An ever present help in times of trouble   **x2**   repeat)

  A(G)   B(A)   A(G)   B(A)
The seas may rise up, the nations may fall
          E(D)   C#ᵐ(Bᵐ)
But there's a city, a holy place,
       F#ᵐ(Eᵐ) F#ᵐ/ E(Eᵐ/D)   B(A)
Where the Most   High   dwells
     C#ᵐ(Bᵐ) G#ᵐ(F#ᵐ)
There's a river, a fortress
     A(G) F#ᵐ(Eᵐ)   B(A)
Therefore we   will not fear

God is our refuge and our strength
An ever present help in times of trouble

Dave Clifton ©1993 IQ Music

WE WORSHIP AND ADORE YOU

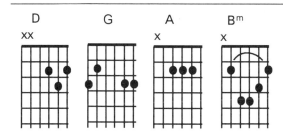

D   G   A   B^m

F
Capo 3rd fret(D)

    F(D)   B^b(G) C(A) F(D)
We worship and adore you,
    B^b(G)   C(A)
Lord hear us when we call
      F(D)   B^b(G) C(A) F(D)
For there is no God above You
    B^b(G)   C(A)   F(D)
You are the Lord of all

But how can we begin to
Express what's on our hearts?
There are not words enough Lord
For us to even start

The tongues of men and angels
We need to sing Your praise
So that we may glorify Your name
Through heaven's eternal days

47

    D^m(B^m)   C(A)   F(D))

There was no other good enough
    B^b(G)   C(A)

To pay the price of sin
    F(D) B^b(G)   C(A)   F(D)

You only could unlock the gate
    B^b(G)   C(A) F(D)

Of heaven and let us in.

A Piercy © 1995 IQ Music

THE LORD REIGNS

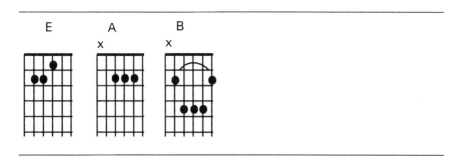

     E
The Lord reigns

Let the earth rejoice   **(x2)**
               A   **B**
Righteousness and truth
                    E
Are the foundations of Your throne   **(x2)**

In Your presence Lord
The mountains melt like wax   **(x2)**
In Your presence Lord
I bow before Your throne   **(x2)**

I lift my hands
To worship You, O Lord   **(x2)**
For You are the Lord
Most high above the earth   **(x2)**

Dan Stradwick © 1980 Scripture In Song / Copycare

I LIFT MY EYES UP

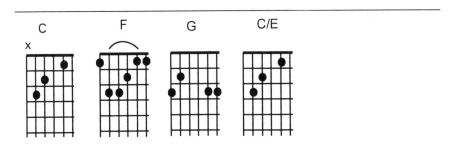

```
C       F     C       F
I lift my eyes up to the mountains
C               F     C    G
Where does my help come from?
C               F        C       F
My help comes from You, Maker of heaven
C       F   C G
Creator of the earth;


C       F           C
O how I need You, Lord
            F       C
You are my only hope
          F C/E  G
You're my only prayer
C           F       C
So I will wait for You
                F       C
To come and rescue me
          F   C/E  G
Come and give me life
```

Brian Doerksen © 1990 Mercy / Vineyard Publishing (adm. Integrity Music Europe Ltd)

FATHER GOD

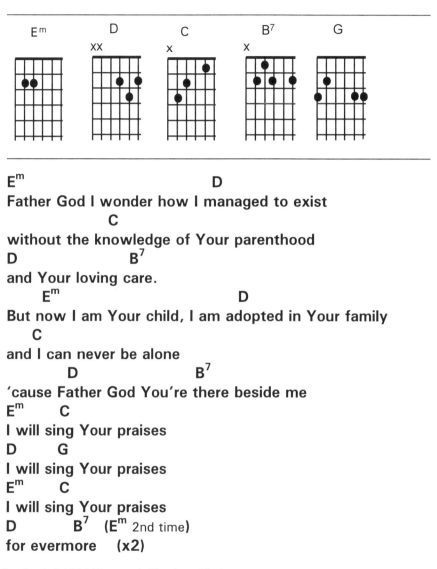

E^m   D

E^m   **D**

Father God I wonder how I managed to exist

                  C

without the knowledge of Your parenthood

D   **B⁷**

and Your loving care.

       E^m   **D**

But now I am Your child, I am adopted in Your family

    C

and I can never be alone

         D   **B⁷**

'cause Father God You're there beside me

E^m   **C**

I will sing Your praises

D   **G**

I will sing Your praises

E^m   **C**

I will sing Your praises

D   **B⁷**   **(E^m 2nd time)**

for evermore   (x2)

Ian Smale © 1984 Kingsway's Thankyou Music

EVERY DAY I LOOK TO YOU

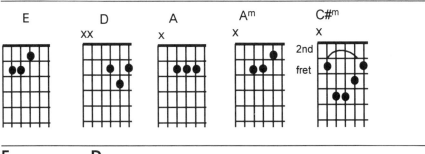

```
E          D
```
Every day I look toYou
```
                A     Aᵐ        E
```
To be the strength   of my life
```
E                 D
```
You're the hope I hold on to
```
                A     Aᵐ      E
```
To be the strength   of my life


```
          A
```
Be the strength of my life
```
        E              (C#ᵐ 2nd time)
```
The strength of my life
```
        A              Aᵐ     E
```
Be the strength of my life today (x2)

Every day I look to You
To be the strength of my life
Breathe on me and make me new
Be the strength of my life

Leslie Phillips © 1984 Word Music (UK)

SING TO THE LORD

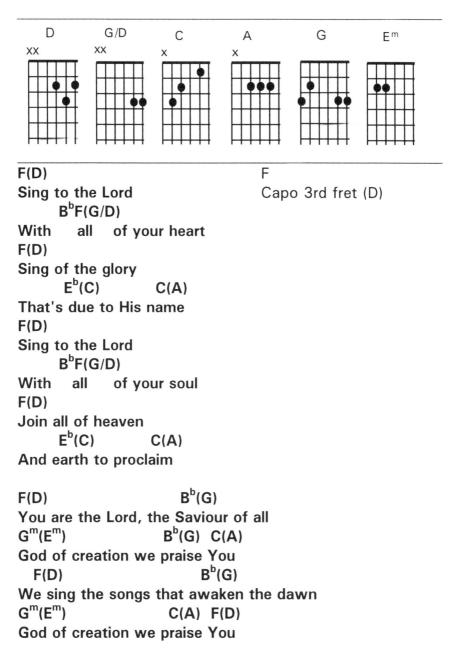

F(D) **F**
Sing to the Lord   Capo 3rd fret (D)
   B^{b}F(G/D)
With   all   of your heart
F(D)
Sing of the glory
   E^b(C)   **C(A)**
That's due to His name
F(D)
Sing to the Lord
   B^{b}F(G/D)
With   all   of your soul
F(D)
Join all of heaven
   E^b(C)   **C(A)**
And earth to proclaim

F(D)   **B^b(G)**
You are the Lord, the Saviour of all
G^m(E^m)   **B^b(G) C(A)**
God of creation we praise You
  F(D)   **B^b(G)**
We sing the songs that awaken the dawn
G^m(E^m)   **C(A) F(D)**
God of creation we praise You

53

Between chorus and verse play:

$G^m(E^m)$ $B^b(G)$ $G^m(E^m)$ $B(G)$

Sing to the Lord
With all of your mind
With understanding
Give thanks to the King
Sing to the Lord
With all of your strength
Living our lives
As a praise offering

Stuart Garrard © 1994 Kingsway's Thankyou Music

I HAVE FOUND SUCH JOY IN MY SALVATION

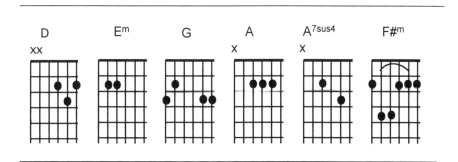

D   Eᵐ   G   A
I have found such joy in my salvation
D   Eᵐ   G   A
Since I gave my life to You
D   Eᵐ   G   A
I have found the reason I'm living
D   Eᵐ   G   A⁷ˢᵘˢ⁴ A
So in love, so near to You.

D Eᵐ   F#ᵐ   G
I worship You, my Lord
D   Eᵐ F#ᵐ   G
With all my life, praise Your name
D Eᵐ   F#ᵐ   G   D   Eᵐ G A
I worship You, worship You, my Lord.

O my Lord, my life I'm giving
A living sacrifice to You.
O my Lord, the reason I'm living,
Is to serve and worship You.

Marc Nelson © 1987 Mercy/ Vineyard Publishing (adm. by Integrity Music Europe Ltd)

PRAISE TO THE LORD THE ALMIGHTY

The King of creation
O my soul, praise Him
For He is thy health and salvation
Come ye who hear
Brothers and sisters draw near
Praise Him in glad adoration

Praise to the Lord, who o'er all
Things so wondrously reigneth
Shelters thee under His wings
Yea, so gently sustaineth:
Hast thou not seen
All that is needful hath been
Granted in what He ordaineth?

Praise to the Lord, who doth
Prosper thy work and defend thee
Surely His goodness and
Mercy shall daily attend thee:
Ponder anew
All the Almighty can do,
He who with love doth befriend thee

Praise to the Lord, O let all
That is in me adore Him
All that hath life and breath
Come now with praises before Him
Let the amen
Sound from His people again
Gladly for aye we adore him

J Neander 1680 Public Domain

GIVE THANKS WITH A GRATEFUL HEART

Give thanks to the Holy One
Give thanks because He's given
Jesus Christ, His Son   (x2)
And now, let the weak say
"I am strong"
Let the poor say
"I am rich"
Because of what the Lord
has done for us   (x2)

Henry Smith © 1978
Integrity's Hosanna! Music / Kingsway's Thankyou Music

WHEN I SURVEY THE WONDROUS CROSS

On which the Prince of Glory died
My richest gain I count but loss
And pour contempt on all my pride

Forbid it, Lord, that I should boast
Save in the death of Christ my God
All the vain things that charm me most
I sacrifice them to his blood

See from His head, His hands, His feet
Sorrow and love flow mingled down
Did e'er such love and sorrow meet
Or thorns compose so rich a crown

Were the whole realm of nature mine
That were an offering far too small
Love so amazing, so divine
Demands my life, my soul, my all

I Watts 1707

HERE IS LOVE VAST AS THE OCEAN

Loving kindness as the flood
When the Prince of Life, our ransom
Shed for us His precious blood

Who His love will not remember?
Who can cease to sing His praise?
He can never be forgotten
Throughout heaven's eternal days

On the mount of crucifixion
Fountains opened deep and wide
Through the floodgates of God's mercy
Flowed a vast and gracious tide

Grace and love, like mighty rivers
Poured incessant from above
And heaven's peace
and perfect justice
Kissed a guilty world in love

William Rees Public Domain

PRAISE GOD FROM WHOM ALL BLESSINGS FLOW

Praise Him all creatures here below
Praise Him above
You heavenly host
Praise Father, Son
and Holy Ghost

Give glory to the Father
Give glory to the Son
Give glory to the Spirit
While endless ages run

"Worthy the Lamb"
all heaven cries
To be exalted thus
"Worthy the Lamb" our hearts reply
For He was slain for us

A. Piercy & D. Clifton © 1993
IQ music

GIVE YOUR THANKS TO THE RISEN SON (echo)
To the Holy and Anointed One (echo)
Who fills our hearts with a joyful song (echo)
Jesus (echo)

Turn to Him, don't be afraid (echo)
Give Him honour, give Him praise (echo)
Lift Him up to the highest place (echo)
Jesus (echo)

Worship Him
Crown Him King
And give Him all your heart (x2)

Dave Bilbrough © 1994 Kingsway's
Thankyou Music

AMAZING GRACE
how sweet the sound
That saved a wretch like me
I once was lost but now am found
Was blind but now I see

'Twas grace that taught
my heart to fear
And grace my fears relieved
How precious did that grace appear
The hour I first believed

Through many dangers,
toils and snares
I have already come
'Tis grace that brought me safe
thus far
And grace will lead me home

When we've been there ten thousand years
Bright shining as the sun
We've no less days to sing God's praise
Than when we first begun

John Newton (1725-1807)
Public Domain

ALMIGHTY GOD

To whom all hearts be open
All desires known
And from whom
no secrets are hidden
Cleanse the thoughts of our hearts
by the inspiration of Your Holy Spirit

That we may perfectly love You
And worthily magnify   (x 2)
Your holy name
Through Christ our Lord, Amen
Through Christ our Lord, Amen

A. Piercy, D. Clifton & C. Groves © 1994 I.Q. Music
Words - The Alternative Service Book 1980
The Central Board of Finance of the Church of England

GOD IS OUR REFUGE

and our strength
An ever present help
in times of trouble

The seas may rise up
The nations may fall
But there's a city
a holy place
Where the Most High dwells
There's a river, a fortress
Therefore we will not fear

God is our refuge
and our strength
An ever present help
in times of trouble

Dave Clifton © 1993 IQ Music

WE WORSHIP AND ADORE YOU

Lord hear us when we call
For there is no God above You
You are the Lord of all

But how can we begin to
Express what's on our hearts
There are not words enough Lord
For us to even start

The tongues of men and angels
We need to sing Your praise
So that we may glorify Your name
Through heaven's eternal days

There was no other good enough
To pay the price of sin
You only could unlock the gate
Of heaven and let us in.

A. Piercy © 1995 IQ Music

THE LORD REIGNS

	(echo)	
Let the earth rejoice	(echo)	(x2)

Righteousness and truth	(echo)	
Are the foundations of Your throne	(echo)	(x2)

In Your presence Lord	(echo)	
The mountains melt like wax	(echo)	(x2)

In Your presence Lord	(echo)	
I bow before your throne	(echo)	(x2)

I lift my hands	(echo)	
And worship You, O Lord	(echo)	(x2)

For You are the Lord	(echo)	
Most high above the earth	(echo)	(x2)

Dan Stradwick © 1980 Scripture In Song / Copycare

I LIFT MY EYES UP
To the mountains
Where does my help come from?
My help comes from You
Maker of heaven
Creator of the earth

O how I need You, Lord
You are my only hope
You're my only prayer
So I will wait for You
To come and rescue me
Come and give me life

Brian Doerksen © 1990 Mercy / Vineyard Publishing (adm. Integrity Music
Europe Ltd)

FATHER GOD I WONDER

How I managed to exist
Without the knowledge
Of Your parenthood
And Your loving care
But now I am Your child
I am adopted in Your family
And I can never be alone
'cause Father God
You're there beside me
I will sing Your praises   (x3)
For evermore   (repeat)

Ian Smale © 1984 Kingsway's Thank-you Music

EVERY DAY I LOOK TO YOU
To be the strength of my life
You're the hope I hold on to
To be the strength of my life

Be the strength of my life
The strength of my life
Be the strength of my life today　　　　　*(x2)*

Every day I look to you
To be the strength of my life
Breathe on me and make me new
Be the strength of my life

SING TO THE LORD
With all of your heart
Sing of the glory
That's due to His name
Sing to the Lord
With all of your soul
Join all of heaven
And earth to proclaim

You are the Lord, the Saviour of all
God of creation we praise You
We sing the songs that awaken the dawn
God of creation we praise You

Sing to the Lord
With all of your mind
With understanding
Give thanks to the King
Sing to the Lord
With all of your strength
Living our lives
As a praise offering

Stuart Garrard © 1994 Kingsway's Thankyou Music

I HAVE FOUND SUCH JOY IN MY SALVATION
Since I gave my heart to You
I have found the reason I'm living
So in love, so near to You.

I worship You, my Lord
With all my life, praise Your name
I worship You, worship You
My Lord.

O my Lord, my life I'm giving
A living sacrifice to You.
O my Lord, the reason I'm living,
Is to serve and worship You.

Marc Nelson © 1987 Mercy/Vineyard Publishing adm. by Integrity Music Europe Ltd)